CAPED CRUSADER CLASSICS

JUDGE DREDD GRAPHIC PAPERBACKS

versus

TITAN BOOKS

THE CHARACTER OF BATMAN WAS CREATED BY

BOB KANE

BATMAN vs CATWOMAN
ISBN 1 85286 125 8

Published by
Titan Books Ltd
58 St Giles High Street
London WC2H 8LH

First Titan Edition February 1989
10 9 8 7 6 5 4 3 2 1

Cover designed by Rian Hughes

Printed by Cox & Wyman Ltd, Reading, Berkshire.

IN GOTHAM CITY, WEALTHY BRUCE WAYNE AND HIS WARD, YOUNG DICK GRAYSON, LOOK AT A CERTAIN PET SHOP WITH UNUSUAL INTEREST...

BRUCE, EVERY TIME WE PASS HERE, I FIND IT HARD TO BELIEVE THAT SELINA KYLE, A RESPECTED SHOP OWNER, WAS ONCE THE NOTORIOUS *CATWOMAN!*

PET SHOP

CATS A SPECIALTY

SELINA KYLE PROPRIETORESS

WELL, REMEMBER, DICK, SELINA WAS AN *AMNESIA VICTIM* DURING HER *CATWOMAN* CAREER! SHE REALLY WASN'T A CRIMINAL AT HEART! AND SPEAKING OF CRIME, IT'S GETTING LATE...TIME WE DID SOME CRIME-HUNTING AS *BATMAN* AND *ROBIN!*

AND WHILE THE CLERKS BUSY THEMSELVES WITH THE FELINE INVASION, A **CLAWLIKE HAND** REACHES FOR A DISPLAY OF VALUABLE BROOCHES!

NEXT,....A WHISTLED SIGNAL...THE CATS RUSH TO THE BIG, BECKONING CLAW, AND...

NOW TO SLIP THESE BROOCHES INTO THEIR BAGS!

ABRUPTLY, THE BIZARRE FIGURE LEAPS INTO AN INCREDIBLE VEHICLE, AND...

TOO BAD YOU DIDN'T BRING YOUR **BATMOBILE!** I WOULD LIKE TO HAVE MATCHED ITS SPEED AGAINST MY **KITTY-CAR!**

Beverly's DRESS SHOPPE

ROBIN, THERE GOES TROUBLE! IF THAT MAN IS OUT TO SET HIMSELF UP AS KING OF THE UNDER-WORLD, WE'LL BE A COUPLE OF VERY BUSY CRIMEFIGHTERS!

WELL, AT LEAST YOU STOPPED HIM FROM GETTING THOSE DIAMOND BROOCHES! SO WE'VE WON THE FIRST ROUND!

AND ONE MORNING, SHORTLY AFTER...

I THINK IT'S TIME WE HAD A TALK WITH SELINA KYLE, *ROBIN!* AS THE EX-*CATWOMAN*, SHE MAY BE ABLE TO GIVE US SOME TIPS ABOUT FIGHTING THE *KING OF THE CATS!*

GOOD IDEA, *BATMAN!*

PET SH
CATS A SPECIALTY

*L*ATER, IN SELINA'S SHOP...

WELL, SELINA, WHAT DO YOU THINK ABOUT YOUR IMITATOR?

I SUPPOSE IF I WERE STILL A CRIMINAL, I WOULD BE INTERESTED IN MEETING HIM! YOU MUST ADMIT, HE IS A DARING SCOUNDREL!

THAT NIGHT, A MEWING CAT STROLLS INTO A ROOM IN A GREAT CHEMICAL PLANT...

WELL, HERE NOW, LITTLE PUSSY CAT, HOW DID YOU GET IN HERE? YOU ARE A PRETTY ONE, AREN'T YOU?

AFFECTIONATELY, THE GUARD STROKES THE ANIMAL'S SOFT, SILKY FUR. A FEW MOMENTS LATER, A DOOR OPENS, AND...

HUH? TH-THE CAT KING!

GRABBING A HUGE BLOCK OF LOOSE STONE, THE CUNNING CRIMINAL STEPS INTO EMPTY SPACE!
OF COURSE! HE USED AN OLD CIRCUS TRICK! THE HEAVY BLOCK OF STONE ACTS LIKE A PLUMMET, CARRYING HIS BODY DOWN STRAIGHT, SO THAT IT CLEAVES THE WATERS NEATLY!

BUT SUDDENLY, THE UNFORESEEN, AS **ROBIN** TRIPS, AND...

ROBIN!

SORRY TO DO THIS...BUT YOU'VE GOT TO EXPECT AN OFF-DAY ONCE IN A WHILE!

CLUNK!

THEN, WITH THE VENGEFUL **BATMAN** IN HOT PURSUIT... THE BANDIT KING FLEES DOWN THE RAMP LEADING TO THE LOWER CAGES...

...LANDING AMIDST A PAIR OF **CAGED JUNGLE BEASTS!**

ARRGH-H-H

HELPLESSLY, THE DAZED MEN WATCH THE SNARLING ANIMALS APPROACH...WHILE UP ABOVE, ANOTHER FIGURE WATCHES WITH HORRIFIED EYES ...THE **CATWOMAN!**

OH! I ARRIVED TOO LATE! IT'S IMPOSSIBLE FOR ME TO SAVE ONE WITHOUT SACRIFICING THE OTHER!

ONE EVENING AS GOTHAM CITY'S VAUNTED LAWMEN, **BATMAN** AND **ROBIN THE BOY WONDER**, LEAVE POLICE HEADQUARTERS AFTER A ROUTINE VISIT...

HELLO, FOLEY! LOOKS LIKE WE'VE GOT SOME PRETTY BAD WEATHER OUTSIDE, EH?

BATMAN! DID YOU EVER HEAR THE EXPRESSION-- "IT'S RAINING CATS AND DOGS"? WELL-- IT'S RAINING **CATS** OUTSIDE RIGHT NOW-- AND I AIN'T KIDDIN'!

A MOMENT LATER...

GOSH! FOLEY WAS RIGHT! LOOK AT ALL THOSE PAPER CATS! WHAT DO YOU MAKE OF IT, **BATMAN?**

HMM-- I HAVE AN IDEA-- AND I HOPE I'M WRONG! LET'S HAVE A CLOSER LOOK AT ONE OF THOSE CATS, **ROBIN!**

THE *CATWOMAN* OPERATES OUT OF A HIDEOUT SHE CALLS HER *CATACOMB.* THIS IS HER *KITTY CAR*-- WHICH I MUST ADMIT IS ALMOST THE EQUAL OF THE *BATMOBILE!*

SEE THE *CAT-OF-NINE-TAILS* SHE'S BRANDISHING? IT'S A WEAPON SHE PUTS TO A DOZEN DIFFERENT USES!

CATWOMAN AND KITTY CAR

HMM-- NOT MUCH USE LOOKING AT THIS PICTURE. NOW THAT THE *CATWOMAN* HAS RETURNED TO CRIME, WE CAN FORGET ABOUT SELINA KYLE!

THIS IS WHAT THE *CATWOMAN* LOOKS LIKE IN REAL LIFE-- A TRULY BEAUTIFUL GIRL NAMED SELINA KYLE, WHO USED TO OPERATE A PET SHOP!

AH, BUT CAN WE, BATMAN? OR ARE YOU IN FOR THE SURPRISE OF YOUR LIFE ??!!

SUDDENLY...

BRUCE! AM I SEEING THINGS? THE FIFTH CONTESTANT IS *SELINA KYLE!* *THE CATWOMAN!*

OF ALL THE BRAZEN...! COME ON, DICK-- WE'VE GOT SOME INQUIRIES TO MAKE!

SELINA KYLE

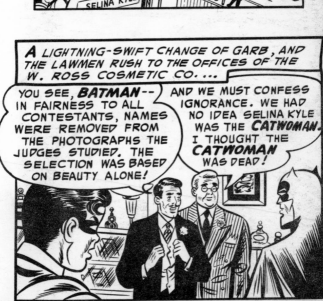

A LIGHTNING-SWIFT CHANGE OF GARB, AND THE LAWMEN RUSH TO THE OFFICES OF THE W. ROSS COSMETIC CO....

YOU SEE, *BATMAN*-- IN FAIRNESS TO ALL CONTESTANTS, NAMES WERE REMOVED FROM THE PHOTOGRAPHS THE JUDGES STUDIED. THE SELECTION WAS BASED ON BEAUTY ALONE!

AND WE MUST CONFESS IGNORANCE. WE HAD NO IDEA SELINA KYLE WAS THE *CATWOMAN.* I THOUGHT THE *CATWOMAN* WAS DEAD!

NEXT DAY, AS **BATMAN** AND **ROBIN** VISIT SELINA KYLE'S SHOP AS PART OF A PRE-ARRANGED PLAN TO KEEP HER UNDER SURVEILLANCE...

REPORTERS, PHOTOGRAPHERS, DOCTORS-- WHAT'S GOING ON HERE?

AMAZING! SELINA KYLE HAS DEVELOPED A RARE BUT HARMLESS TYPE OF **SLEEPING SICKNESS!** SHE HAS BECOME A MODERN-DAY **SLEEPING BEAUTY!**

AND AS THE LAWMEN ENTER THE SHOP...

THE W. ROSS CO. PAID FOR THIS FANCY SHOWCASE-- SO THAT THE MEDICAL PROFESSION COULD OBSERVE THIS RARE MALADY-- AND OF COURSE, FOR THE PUBLICITY TOO!

WELL, AT LEAST THIS WILL KEEP THE **CATWOMAN** QUIET FOR A WHILE!

NEXT EVENING...

5¢

GOTHAM GAZETTE

SLEEPING BEAUTY PASSES QUIET DAY "NO CHANGE"

SAY DOCTORS WHO REMAIN OPTIMISTIC EXPECT MALADY TO LINGER THRE OR FOUR WEEKS TO LEAVE NO ILL EFFECTS

"QUEEN FOR A DAY" WINNER TO BE ANNOUN NEXT WEE GALA FESTI

LATER THAT NIGHT, IN THE APARTMENT OF NANCY BROOKS...

THE--THE CATWOMAN!

DON'T BE ALARMED, SISTER! I JUST HAVE A LITTLE GAS FOR YOU TO INHALE! YOU WON'T FEEL A THING, I PROMISE YOU! HA-HA!

AND EVEN LATER THAT SAME FATEFUL EVENING AS DIANE OLSON RETURNS HOME FROM THE THEATRE...

¡GASP¿ ¡GURGLE!¿

NO SCREAMING, PLEASE! I THINK IT'S TIME YOU-- WENT TO SLEEP-- A GOOD *LONG* SLEEP! HA-HA!

MINUTES LATER, AS THE HUGE RADAR GRID IN THE *BAT-CAVE* ATTRACTS *ROBIN'S* ATTENTION...

BATMAN-- THIS IS AMAZING! ONLY ONE GROUND VEHICLE BESIDE THE *BATMOBILE* IS LARGE ENOUGH AND FAST ENOUGH TO SEND OUT THE IMPULSES THIS GRID IS PICKING UP! THE *CATWOMAN'S KITTY CAR!*

WE'LL SOON FIND OUT IF IT'S THE *KITTY CAR!* COME ON-- LET'S PAY A VISIT TO SELINA KYLE! SHE'S SUPPOSED TO BE UNDER SPECIAL GUARD, IN HER GLASS TOMB!

THEN, AS THE **LAWMEN** DEPART...

WELL, WHAT DO YOU THINK NOW?

I'M PUZZLED! PARTICULARLY BY A SMALL, QUICK **FLASH OF LIGHT** I SAW WHILE WE WERE WATCHING SELINA. CAN'T FIGURE OUT WHERE IT COULD HAVE COME FROM. OH, WELL, WE MUST HAVE BEEN WRONG ABOUT THAT **KITTY CAR!**

NEXT DAY, A BOMBSHELL HITS GOTHAM CITY...

GOTHAM 💫 GAZETTE 5¢

TWO NEW SLEEPING BEAUTIES
SECOND AND THIRD
"QUEEN FOR A DAY" CONTESTANTS SUCCUMB TO STRANGE DISEASE

W. ROSS AND C
SPOKESMAN FEA
FOR REMAINING
CONTESTANTS. 9
ALL GIRLS MAY

AND AS **BATMAN** FOLLOWS THE **CATWOMAN** INTO THE WINDOW OF THE BUILDING ACROSS THE COURTYARD...

SO THE **MOUSE** FOLLOWED THE **CAT** RIGHT INTO THE TRAP! I FIGURED YOU'D SHOW UP AT BOBBY SHAW'S APARTMENT, **BATMAN**--- AND I WAS READY FOR YOU!

BOSS, EVERYTHING'S SET UP OVER AT THE **HOUSE-WARES EXHIBIT** LIKE YOU ORDERED! LET'S GET GOIN'!

SOON AFTER, AT THE **HOUSEWARES EXHIBIT**, CLOSED TO THE PUBLIC FOR THE EVENING...

WILDCATS, **BATMAN!** WHEN WE LET THEM LOOSE IN THE TRENCH OF THIS ORANGE JUICE SQUEEZER, WE OUGHT TO HAVE SOME FUN! THEY CAN'T GET UP TO YOU--THE GLASS IS TOO SLIPPERY-- NOR CAN THEY GET OUT! BUT **YOU'D** BETTER NOT LEAVE YOUR PERCH, UNLESS YOU WANT TO BE TORN APART!

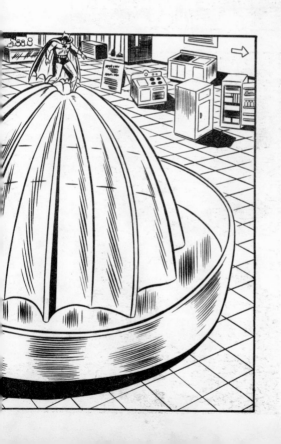

KICKING OUT A HOLE IN THE TOP OF THE SQUEEZER, **BATMAN** LOWERS HIMSELF THROUGH IT-- STILL SHIELDED FROM THE WILDCATS BY A WALL OF THICK GLASS!

NOW TO CAREFULLY LIFT AN EDGE OF THIS THING, AND WRIGGLE OUT TO FREEDOM!

AT LEAST THEY LEFT MY **UTILITY BELT** NEARBY-- I'LL CONTACT **ROBIN** IMMEDIATELY!

SOMETIME LATER, AS CONTACT IS RE-ESTABLISHED BETWEEN **BATMAN** AND **ROBIN**, AND THEY MEET ON A GOTHAM CITY STREET CORNER...

...WHILE THE TWO REMAINING CONTESTANTS IN THE "QUEEN FOR A DAY" CONTEST HAVE SUCCUMBED TO SLEEPING SICKNESS, **SELINA KYLE** HAS AWAKENED IN GOOD HEALTH! AS THE ONLY AVAILABLE CONTESTANT, SHE WILL BE NAMED **QUEEN** TODAY!

COME ON, **ROBIN** -- THAT CEREMONY IS SCHEDULED TO GO OFF AT ANY MINUTE!

AND AT THE GOTHAM CENTRE, WHERE THE ELABORATE FESTIVITIES ATTENDING THE CROWNING OF THE *BEAUTY QUEEN* ARE IN PROGRESS...

AHH, HERE COMES OUR MESSENGER FROM PARIS, WITH YOUR SPECIAL GIFT OF PERFUME!

{SNIFF, SNIFF} THAT'S FUNNY! I CAN SMELL THE *SCENT* OF THAT PERFUME QUITE PLAINLY!

ROBIN, ANY GOOD PERFUME BOTTLE IS *HERMETICALLY SEALED* AT THE FACTORY TO PREVENT EVAPORATION. THE FACT THAT I CAN SMELL *THIS* PERFUME MEANS THE BOTTLE HAS BEEN *TAMPERED* WITH!

BUT WHAT DOES THAT MEAN?

QUEEN FOR A DAY

WATCHING HIS CHANCE, **BATMAN** CLUMSILY TRIPS AGAINST SELINA, KNOCKING THE **PERFUME BOTTLE** OUT OF HER HANDS!

WHY, **LOOK!** **DIAMONDS!** A FORTUNE IN **DIAMONDS!**

YES! A CLEVER **SMUGGLING SCHEME** NIPPED IN THE BUD!

THE **CATWOMAN** KNEW THAT THE WINNER WOULD RECEIVE SPECIAL PERFUME! IT WAS EASY FOR HER AGENTS IN EUROPE TO SWITCH BOTTLES ON THE UNSUSPECTING ENVOY, AND GIVE HIM THE ONE CONTAINING THE DIAMONDS!

THE CROOKS KNEW THAT THE ENVOY WOULD NEVER BE SUSPECTED BY **CUSTOM OFFICIALS** AND WOULD GET THROUGH WITHOUT ANY INSPECTION!

LATER, AFTER THE **CATWOMAN** HAS BEEN TAKEN INTO CUSTODY...

WHEN THE **CATWOMAN** DISCOVERED THIS GAS THAT WOULD INDUCE SLEEPING SICKNESS, SHE WAS READY TO PUT HER PLAN INTO ACTION!

BY GIVING HERSELF A SMALL DOSE, SHE FOOLED THE DOCTORS. AFTER THAT, SHE USED **CATOPTRICS**, SNEAKING OUT OF THE SHOWCASE DURING THE CHANGE OF GUARD, AND TURNING ON HER PROJECTOR!

AND IN A SPECIAL WING OF GOTHAM HOSPITAL...

THE **SLEEPING BEAUTIES** OF GOTHAM CITY! THEY'LL SOON AWAKEN, WITH A STORY TO TELL FOR THE REST OF THEIR LIVES!

THE END

A PLANE MAKES A ROUTINE LANDING AT A SMALL GOTHAM CITY AIRPORT ---

--- AND ITS PILOT GETS A FEARFUL WELCOME!

WHAT-- A BLACK PANTHER-- *HELP!*

A SWIFT CHANGE, AND PLAYBOY BRUCE WAYNE AND HIS WARD, DICK GRAYSON, BECOME *BATMAN* AND *ROBIN* THE *BOY WONDER!*

WE'LL GET THE *BATPLANE* OUT AND GO STRAIGHT TO THAT AIRFIELD!

SHE'LL BE GONE-- SHE STRIKES AS FAST AS THE CATS SHE LOVES!

AT THE AIRFIELD, *BATMAN* AND *ROBIN* HEAR AN INCREDIBLE STORY!

YOU SAY SHE USES A HUGE BLACK *PANTHER* IN HER ROBBERY? HOW COULD EVEN *CATWOMAN* CONTROL SUCH A BEAST?

IT'S UNCANNY! HMM--- IF WE HAD SOME CLUE TO WHERE SHE WENT, THE *BATPLANE* MIGHT STILL OVERTAKE HER!

THE TRAINED EYES OF THE WORLD'S GREATEST SLEUTHS DISCOVER WHAT OTHERS MIGHT HAVE MISSED!

WHEW-- THAT'S A RELIEF! I WAS AFRAID SHE'D SEE US IN THAT SHALLOW WATER, BUT SHE DIDN'T!

DIDN'T SHE, *ROBIN?* I WONDER! ANYWAY, WE'VE GOT WORK TO DO --- COME ON!

THEN, AS NIGHT BLANKETS THE JUNGLE, TWO EERIE FIGURES FOLLOW ON THE TRACK OF THE GREAT CATS!

WE CAN SOLVE THE MYSTERY OF THE DIAMOND MINE LATER -- AND TAKE CARE OF THOSE CROOKS! BUT RIGHT NOW I WANT TO FIND *CATWOMAN'S* SECRET LAIR-- AND THESE TRACKS SHOULD LEAD US THERE!

I STILL DON'T GET IT! WILD LIONS, TIGERS, AND LEOPARDS-- HOW DOES SHE CONTROL THEM, ANYWAY?

PRESENTLY, SCOUTING AROUND THE AWESOME RUIN, *BATMAN* FINDS WHAT HE EXPECTED!

THESE ARE CIRCUS ANIMALS--- BROUGHT HERE BY *CATWOMAN!* AND THAT GIVES ME AN IDEA! LISTEN, *ROBIN*---

I'LL BE READY-- BUT BE CAREFUL, *BATMAN!* IF IT DOESN'T WORK---

I'M RELYING ON THE FACT THEY WERE CIRCUS ANIMALS, TO MAKE IT WORK!

UNKNOWN TO **BATMAN**, THE VERY CRIMINAL OF WHOM HE SPEAKS IS CLOSE AT HAND!

CATWOMAN FAILED TO GET HIM -- AND HE'S GOT *HER!* IF I SHOOT ONE OF THE DUO, THE OTHER MIGHT GET ME --- I'LL USE SOMETHING THAT WILL GET THEM **BOTH!**

RUTHLESS IN STRATEGY, THE EVIL JARROW UNLEASHES A THING OF TERROR...

THIS GORILLA MAY DESTROY *CATWOMAN*, TOO, BUT I DON'T CARE AS LONG AS IT GETS **BATMAN** AND **ROBIN!**

ROBIN'S UNCONSCIOUS, BUT IT'S DROPPED HIM-- NOW IT'S AFTER ME--

WHIRLING THE BURNING BRAND IN CIRCLES, *BATMAN* DRIVES BACK THE RAGING MONSTER!

IT'S RECOILING INTO ITS CAGE-- NOW TO SLAM THE DOOR QUICK!

GOT MY HANDS FREE--BUT I CAN'T SWIM OUT OF THIS TERRIFIC CURRENT IN TIME TO ESCAPE THE FALLS! ONLY ONE CHANCE--THE SILKEN ROPE IN MY UTILITY BELT!

IF I CAN GET A NOOSE OF MY ROPE OVER A PROJECTING ROCK IN THE BOTTOM-- GOT IT! AND JUST IN TIME, FOR I'M RIGHT AT THE FALLS!

BUT MEANWHILE, A GREAT CAT HAS GONE LOYALLY TO ITS MISTRESS...

MY FAITHFUL PET-- YOUR SHARP CLAWS ARE HELPFUL NOW, THOUGH YOU DON'T KNOW IT!

AND WHEN THE DYNAMIC DUO FINISHES SECURING THE CROOKS, THEY GET AN AMAZING SURPRISE!

CATWOMAN! SHE'S GETTING AWAY, TO HER HIDDEN PLANE!

AND WE CAN'T FOLLOW TILL THE BATPLANE IS REPAIRED! I GUESS SHE ESCAPES US FOR NOW, THOUGH WE'VE BROKEN UP HER CRIME-SCHEME!

These yarns created a
Bat-sensation in the '60s.
Now, Titan presents the
best of these Bat-tales in
an eminently collectable
series designed to fit into
any utility belt — and at
a price to match!

Born in the war-torn forties. Born to live in the shadows. To stalk, to avenge, to punish.
He was and always will be the terror of Gotham City... The Dark Knight! Absorb his most powerful adventures in these Titan graphic novels.